PhonicsWorks™
Assessments Basic

Illustrations Credits
All illustrations © K12 unless otherwise noted

About K12 Inc.
K12 Inc., a technology-based education company, is the nation's leading provider of proprietary curriculum and online education programs to students in grades K–12. K^{12} provides its curriculum and academic services to online schools, traditional classrooms, blended school programs, and directly to families. K12 Inc. also operates the K^{12} International Academy, an accredited, diploma-granting online private school serving students worldwide. K^{12}'s mission is to provide any child the curriculum and tools to maximize success in life, regardless of geographic, financial, or demographic circumstances. K12 Inc. is accredited by CITA. More information can be found at www.K12.com.

978-1-60153-187-2
Printed by Action Printing, Fond du Lac, WI, USA, April 2018

Contents

☼ Unit Checkpoint
Sounds /m/, /t/, /n/, /p/, /h/, /ē/, /d/, and /ŏ/

Part 1. Beginning, Middle, or End?

Color the beginning car black. Color the middle car yellow.
Color the ending car red.

1.　　　**2.**　　　**3.**

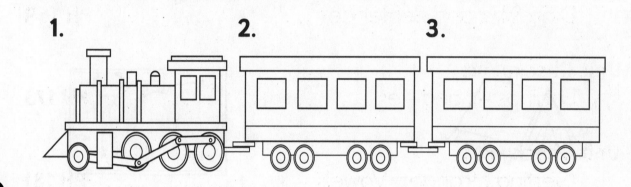

Part 2. Match Beginning Sounds

Draw a line to connect the pictures that begin with the same sound.

4.  • •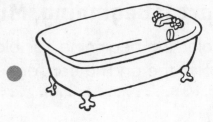

5.  • •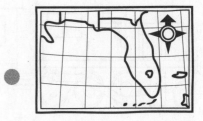

6.  • •

7. 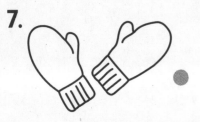 • •

Part 3. Beginning Sounds

Listen to the group of words. Say which words begin with the same sound.

8.

9.

10.

11.

12.

13.

14.

15.

Part 4. Ending Sounds

Listen to the group of words. Say which words end with the same sound.

16.

17.

18.

19.

20.

21.

☼ Unit Checkpoint
Sounds /b/, /f/, /ā/, /g/, /ō/, and /j/

Part 1. Letter Matching

Read across the row from left to right. Circle the letters that match the first letter in the row.

1.	a	o	a	b	d	a
2.	b	d	c	a	b	b
3.	c	d	a	c	c	b
4.	d	a	d	c	d	a

Part 2. Match Ending Sounds

Draw a line to connect the pictures that end with the same sound.

PHONICS

5.

6.

7.

8.

Part 3. Rhymes

Listen to the pair of words. Do the words rhyme?

9.

10.

11.

12.

13.

14.

Part 4. Beginning Sounds

Listen to the group of words. Say which words begin with the same sound.

15.

16.

17.

18.

19.

20.

PHONICS

☼ Unit Checkpoint
Sounds /s/, /ă/, /w/, /z/, /ī/, and /l/

Part 1. Letter Matching

Read across the row from left to right. Circle the letters that match the first letter in the row.

1.	e	a	e	c	g	e
2.	g	f	h	g	e	g
3.	f	d	f	a	f	b
4.	h	e	g	h	f	h

Part 2. Match Ending Sounds

Draw a line to connect the pictures that end with the same sound.

5.  ● ●

6.  ● ●

7.  ● ●

8.  ● ●

Part 3. Rhymes

Listen to the pair of words. Do the words rhyme?

9.

10.

11.

12.

13.

14.

PHONICS

Part 4. Beginning Sounds

Listen to the group of words. Say which words begin with the same sound.

15.

16.

17.

18.

19.

20.

☼ Unit Checkpoint
Sounds /th/, /<u>th</u>/, /ĕ/, /k/, /v/, and /r/

Part 1. Letter Matching

Read across the row from left to right. Circle the letters that match the first letter in the row.

1.	i	j	i	k	l	i
2.	j	i	j	g	j	i
3.	k	f	a	k	h	k
4.	l	b	e	l	j	l

Part 2. Match Ending Sounds

Draw a line to connect the pictures that end with the same sound.

5.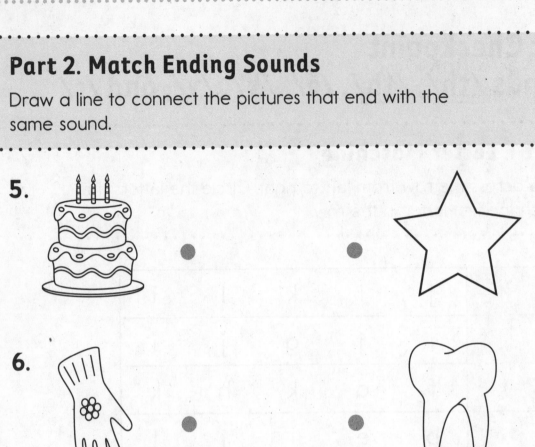

6.

7.

8.

Name .... Date ....

Part 3. Rhymes

Listen to the pair of words. Do the words rhyme?

9.

10.

11.

12.

13.

14.

Part 4. Middle Sounds

Listen to the pair of words. Do the words have the same middle sound?

15.

16.

17.

18.

19.

20.

PHONICS

Part 5. Onset and Rime

Listen to the sounds. Then, say the whole word.

21.

22.

23.

24.

25.

26.

PHONICS

☼ Unit Checkpoint
Sounds /ĭ/, /ŭ/, /ch/, and /y/

Part 1. Letter Matching

Read across the row from left to right. Circle the letter or letters that match the first letter in the row.

1.	m	n	m	b	f	m
2.	n	m	p	n	d	u
3.	o	c	d	o	q	m
4.	p	b	p	d	q	p
5.	q	d	f	q	g	q

Part 2. Match Middle Sounds

Draw a line to connect the pictures that have the same middle sound.

6.  ● ●

7.  ● ●

8.  ● ●

9.  ● ●

Part 3. Rhymes

Listen to the pair of words. Do the words rhyme?

10.

11.

12.

13.

14.

15.

PHONICS

Part 4. Beginning Sounds

Listen to the pair of words. Do the words have the same beginning sound?

16.

17.

18.

19.

20.

21.

Part 5. Onset and Rime

Listen to the sounds. Then, say the whole word.

22.

23.

24.

25.

26.

27.

PHONICS

☼ Unit Checkpoint
Sounds /sh/, /aw/, & /kw/ and Syllables

Part 1. Letter Matching

Read across the row from left to right. Circle the letter or letters that match the first letter in the row.

1.	t	o	s	t	r	u
2.	u	u	r	s	t	q
3.	r	p	u	r	s	r
4.	s	t	s	s	r	u
5.	p	n	p	o	q	m

Part 2. Match Beginning Sounds

Draw a line to connect the pictures that begin with the same sound.

6.

 ● ●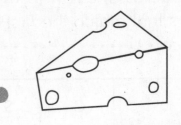

7.

 ● ●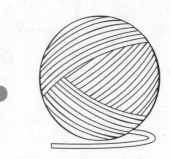

8.

 ● ●

Part 3. Rhymes

Listen to the pair of words. Do the words rhyme?

9.

10.

11.

12.

13.

14.

Part 4. Beginning Sounds

Listen to the group of words. Say which words begin with the same sound.

15.

16.

17.

18.

19.

20.

21.

22.

Part 5. Onset and Rime

Listen to the sounds. Then, say the whole word.

23.

24.

25.

26.

27.

28.

PHONICS

PHONICS

Part 6. Blend Sounds

Listen to the sounds. Then, say the whole word.

29.

30.

31.

32.

33.

34.

Part 7. Syllables

Listen to the word. Repeat the word. Fist tap the word to help you count the number of syllables.

35.

36.

37.

38.

39.

40.

☼ Unit Checkpoint
Sounds /oi/, /ū/, & /ks/ and Sound Practice

Part 1. Letter Matching

Read across the row from left to right. Circle the letters that match the first letter in the row.

1.	v	u	v	w	x	v
2.	w	v	w	m	w	u
3.	x	s	v	x	s	x
4.	u	u	v	w	u	n
5.	t	l	t	t	k	t

PHONICS

Part 2. Match Ending Sounds

Draw a line to connect the pictures that end with the same sound.

6. 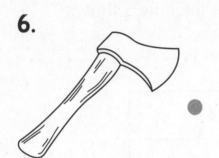 •   • 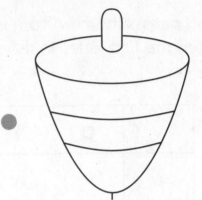

7.  •   • 

8.  •   • 

Part 3. Rhymes

Listen to the pair of words. Do the words rhyme?

9.

10.

11.

12.

13.

14.

Part 4. Beginning Sounds

Listen to the group of words. Say which words begin with the same sound.

15.

16.

17.

18.

19.

20.

21.

22.

Part 5. Onset and Rime

Listen to the sounds. Then, say the whole word.

23.

24.

25.

26.

27.

28.

PHONICS

Part 6. Blend Sounds

Listen to the sounds. Then, say the whole word.

29.

30.

31.

32.

33.

34.

PHONICS

☼ Unit Checkpoint
Sounds Long Double *o* & /ow/ and Sound Practice

Part 1. Letter Matching

Read across the row from left to right. Circle the letter that matches the first letter in the row.

1.	v	u	v	w	x	y
2.	w	n	w	m	b	a
3.	x	k	t	x	w	u
4.	y	h	v	q	u	y
5.	z	f	j	i	z	r

Part 2. Match Middle Sounds

Draw a line to connect the pictures that have the same middle sound.

6.

7.

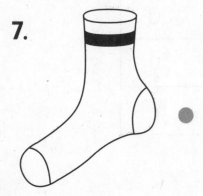

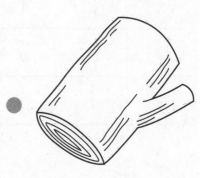

8.

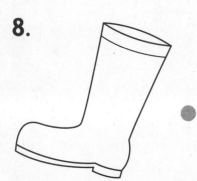

PHONICS

Part 3. Rhymes

Listen to the pair of words. Do the words rhyme?

9.

10.

11.

12.

13.

14.

Part 4. Ending Sounds

Listen to the group of words. Say which words end with the same sound.

15.

16.

17.

18.

19.

20.

21.

22.

Part 5. Onset and Rime

Listen to the sounds. Then, say the whole word.

23.

24.

25.

26.

27.

28.

PHONICS

Part 6. Blend Sounds

Listen to the sounds. Then, say the whole word.

29.

30.

31.

32.

33.

34.

☼ Unit Checkpoint
Sounds for Letters *a, m, s, t, b, f, c, h,* and *j*

Part 1. Say Sounds

Read across the row from left to right. Say a sound that letter makes.

1. a	**2.** b	**3.** c	**4.** m
5. s	**6.** t	**7.** f	**8.** h
9. j	**10.** a	**11.** b	**12.** m
13. c	**14.** t	**15.** f	**16.** s
17. h	**18.** a	**19.** j	**20.** a

Part 2. Word Dissection

Read the word. Circle the letter or groups of letters that spell the sound you are asked to find.

21. c a t

22. j a m

23. c a b

24. m a t

25. t a b

Part 3. Finger Stretching

Listen to the word. Finger stretch the word.

26.

27.

28.

29.

30.

31.

PHONICS

Part 4. Circle the Letter

Listen to the sound. Circle the letter that makes the sound.

32. f   h   t

33. a   b   c

34. m   s   a

35. a   c   m

36. b   j   h

37. h   b   s

38. m   j   c

39. s   f   h

40. a   m   c

PHONICS

Part 5. Read Aloud
Read the sentences aloud.

41.

The cat is fat.

Sam and the cat sat.

The bat has jam.

Part 6. Say Letters

Listen to the sound. Say a letter that makes that sound.

42.	48.	54.
43.	49.	55.
44.	50.	56.
45.	51.	57.
46.	52.	58.
47.	53.	59.

☼ Unit Checkpoint
Sounds for Letters *l*, *n*, *p*, & *r*, Sound Review, and Vowels

Part 1. Say Sounds

Read across the row from left to right. Say a sound that letter makes.

1. a	2. l	3. n	4. p
5. r	6. a	7. n	8. p
9. r	10. l	11. b	12. c
13. a	14. m	15. s	16. t
17. f	18. h	19. j	20. a

Part 2. Word Dissection

Read the word. Circle the letter or groups of letters that spell the sound you are asked to find.

21. n a p

22. r a n

23. p a l

24. p a n

25. r a p

PHONICS

Part 3. Finger Stretching

Listen to the word. Finger stretch the word.

26.

27.

28.

29.

30.

31.

PHONICS

Part 4. Circle the Letter

Listen to the sound. Circle the letter that makes the sound.

32. l n p

33. a m r

34. c n m

35. a b t

36. p h b

37. c b h

38. m s a

39. h j s

PHONICS

Part 5. Read Aloud

Read the sentences aloud.

40.

> The man is in the lab.
>
> Is the fan on?
>
> Nab the cat!
>
> Is the ham in the pan?
>
> Sam and Jan ran a lap.

PHONICS

Part 6. Say Letters

Listen to the sound. Say a letter that makes that sound.

41.

42.

43.

44.

45.

46.

47.

48.

49.

50.

51.

52.

53.

54.

55.

56.

57.

58.

☼ Unit Checkpoint
Sounds for Letters *o*, *d*, *g*, *k*, and *v*

Part 1. Say Sounds

Read across the row from left to right. Say a sound that letter makes.

1. o	**2.** l	**3.** d	**4.** g
5. k	**6.** v	**7.** n	**8.** p
9. r	**10.** o	**11.** a	**12.** d
13. g	**14.** k	**15.** v	**16.** o
17. b	**18.** l	**19.** h	**20.** a

Part 2. Word Dissection

Read the word. Circle the letter or groups of letters that spell the sound you are asked to find.

21. j o g

22. m o p

23. c o d

24. h o t

25. l o g

Part 3. Finger Stretching

Listen to the word. Finger stretch the word.

26.

27.

28.

29.

30.

31.

Part 4. Circle the Letter

Listen to the sound. Circle the letter that makes the sound.

32. b g s

33. a g k

34. k n m

35. b r d

36. p v h

37. d n o

38. n l f

39. r m b

PHONICS

Part 5. Read Aloud

Read the sentences aloud.

40.

> Mom got a job.
>
> It is a hog.
>
> He can jog to the van.
>
> Bob had a hot dog and pop.
>
> Was the fat hog on the cot?

PHONICS

Part 6. Say Letters

Listen to the sound. Say a letter that makes that sound.

41.	47.	53.
42.	48.	54.
43.	49.	55.
44.	50.	56.
45.	51.	57.
46.	52.	58.

PHONICS

☼ Unit Checkpoint
Getting Stronger: Sounds /ă/ and /ŏ/

Part 1. Say Sounds

Read across the row from left to right. Say a sound that letter makes.

1. a	**2.** l	**3.** r	**4.** g
5. o	**6.** v	**7.** o	**8.** p
9. r	**10.** a	**11.** l	**12.** d
13. g	**14.** k	**15.** v	**16.** n
17. k	**18.** o	**19.** h	**20.** a

Part 2. Word Dissection

Read the word. Circle the letter or groups of letters that spell the sound you are asked to find.

21. h o t

22. t o p

23. r a t

24. n o d

25. r a b

Part 3. Finger Stretching

Listen to the word. Finger stretch the word.

26.

27.

28.

29.

PHONICS

Part 4. Circle and Write

Listen to the sound. Circle the letter that makes the sound.
Write the letter.

30. l g b _____

31. m n p _____

32. b f d _____

33. v j r _____

Part 5. Read Aloud

Read the sentences aloud.

34.

> Mom has a tan bag.
>
> Jan can not hop in the fog.
>
> Was the tot mad at Rod?
>
> Dad got a job.
>
> He had a mop.

PHONICS

Part 6. Say Letters

Listen to the sound. Say a letter that makes that sound.

35.	41.	47.
36.	42.	48.
37.	43.	49.
38.	44.	50.
39.	45.	51.
40.	46.	52.

☼ Unit Checkpoint
Sounds for Letters *i*, *qu*, and *z*

Part 1. Say Sounds

Read across the row from left to right. Say a sound that the letter or letters make.

1. i	**2.** qu	**3.** z	**4.** a
5. o	**6.** a	**7.** i	**8.** qu
9. z	**10.** o	**11.** l	**12.** b
13. r	**14.** d	**15.** v	**16.** n
17. p	**18.** i	**19.** g	**20.** i

Part 2. Word Dissection

Read the word. Circle the letter or group of letters that spell the sound you are asked to find.

21. p i g

22. q u i z

23. q u i t

24. z i p

25. z i b

PHONICS

Part 3. Finger Stretching

Listen to the word. Finger stretch the word.

26.

27.

28.

29.

PHONICS

Part 4. Circle and Write

Listen to the sound. Circle the letter or letters that make the sound. Write the letter or letters.

PHONICS

30. z   g   s   _____

31. o   i   a   _____

32. z   k   qu   _____

33. v   j   g   _____

Part 5. Read Aloud

Read the sentences aloud.

34.

> The pig can dig in the pit.
>
> Did he quit the job with Kip?
>
> Mom says I have to hop.
>
> Is the lid on the pot?

PHONICS

Part 6. Say Letters

Listen to the sound. Say the letter or letters that make that sound.

PHONICS

35.	41.	47.
36.	42.	48.
37.	43.	49.
38.	44.	50.
39.	45.	51.
40.	46.	52.

☼ Unit Checkpoint
Getting Stronger: Sounds /ă/, /ĭ/, and /ŏ/

Part 1. Say Sounds

Read across the row from left to right. Say a sound that the letter or letters make.

1. o	**2.** z	**3.** a	**4.** i
5. o	**6.** i	**7.** p	**8.** v
9. qu	**10.** a	**11.** a	**12.** o
13. qu	**14.** v	**15.** k	**16.** z
17. i	**18.** g	**19.** o	**20.** p

Part 2. Word Dissection

Read the word. Circle the letter or group of letters that spell the sound you are asked to find.

21. c a t

22. q u i t

23. l o g

24. p o t

25. q u i b

Part 3. Finger Stretching

Listen to the word. Finger stretch the word.

26.

27.

28.

29.

PHONICS

PHONICS

Part 4. Circle and Write

Listen to the sound. Circle the letter or letters that make the sound. Write the letter or letters.

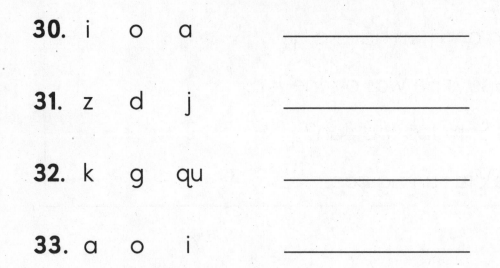

30. i   o   a   _____

31. z   d   j   _____

32. k   g   qu   _____

33. a   o   i   _____

Part 5. Read Aloud

Read the sentences aloud.

34.

The pot has a lid.

Dan and Ron have a quiz.

Tim says he was on the job.

Did Sam tap the can?

The pig ran zig-zag.

PHONICS

Part 6. Say Letters

Listen to the sound. Say the letter or letters that make that sound.

35.	41.	47.
36.	42.	48.
37.	43.	49.
38.	44.	50.
39.	45.	51.
40.	46.	52.

☼ Unit Checkpoint
Sounds for Letters *u*, *w*, and *x*

Part 1. Say Sounds

Read across the row from left to right. Say a sound that the letter or letters make.

1. u	**2.** qu	**3.** w	**4.** a	**5.** o	**6.** x
7. a	**8.** i	**9.** x	**10.** z	**11.** o	**12.** u
13. i	**14.** u	**15.** g	**16.** w	**17.** r	**18.** u

Part 2. Word Dissection

Read the word. Circle the letter or group of letters that spell the sound you are asked to find.

19. s u n

20. m u d

21. t u b

22. r u g

23. d u d

PHONICS

Part 3. Finger Stretching

Listen to the word. Finger stretch the word.

24.

25.

26.

27.

PHONICS

Part 4. Dictation

Listen to the word. Repeat the word, and then write it.

28. _____

29. _____

30. _____

31. _____

PHONICS

Part 5. Read Aloud

Read the sentences aloud.

32.

> Where is the wig?
>
> There is the bug! It is in the cup.
>
> Gus got the gum from the big kid.
>
> Can Bud fix the jug?

PHONICS

Part 6. Say Letters

Listen to the sound. Say the letter or letters that make that sound.

33.	39.	45.
34.	40.	46.
35.	41.	47.
36.	42.	48.
37.	43.	49.
38.	44.	50.

✷ Unit Checkpoint
Getting Stronger: Sounds /ă/, /ĭ/, /ŏ/, and /ŭ/

Part 1. Say Sounds

Read across the row from left to right. Say a sound that the letter or letters make.

1. u	**2.** qu	**3.** w	**4.** a	**5.** o	**6.** x
7. a	**8.** i	**9.** l	**10.** z	**11.** o	**12.** u
13. i	**14.** u	**15.** g	**16.** d	**17.** r	**18.** v

Part 2. Word Dissection

Read the word. Circle the letter or group of letters that spell the sound you are asked to find.

19. f u n

20. h o t

21. r i b

22. w a g

23. q u i t

PHONICS

Part 3. Finger Stretching

Listen to the word. Finger stretch the word.

24.

25.

26.

27.

PHONICS

Part 4. Dictation

Listen to the word. Repeat the word, and then write it.

28. _____

29. _____

30. _____

31. _____

PHONICS

Part 5. Read Aloud

Read the sentences aloud.

32.

> Did the dog dig there?
>
> Where is the mud from?
>
> He can win the cup.
>
> The sun is up.
>
> Is the lad on the bus?

PHONICS

Part 6. Say Letters

Listen to the sound. Say the letter or letters that make that sound.

33.	39.	45.
34.	40.	46.
35.	41.	47.
36.	42.	48.
37.	43.	49.
38.	44.	50.

PHONICS

☼ Unit Checkpoint
Sounds for Letters *e* and *y*

Part 1. Say Sounds

Read across the row from left to right. Say a sound that the letter or letters make.

1. e	**2.** qu	**3.** w	**4.** y	**5.** e	**6.** x
7. a	**8.** i	**9.** x	**10.** y	**11.** o	**12.** u
13. i	**14.** u	**15.** y	**16.** w	**17.** y	**18.** e

Part 2. Word Dissection

Read the word. Circle the letter or group of letters that spell the sound you are asked to find.

19. b e d

20. y e s

21. s e t

22. v e t

23. y e t

Part 3. Finger Stretching

Listen to the word. Finger stretch the word.

24.

25.

26.

27.

Part 4. Dictation

Listen to the word. Repeat the word, and then write it.

PHONICS

28. _____

29. _____

30. _____

31. _____

Part 5. Read Aloud

Read the sentences aloud.

32.

> Put Ken to bed.
>
> The jet is from Ben.
>
> Jeb can run from the hen.
>
> Yes, his leg got wet.
>
> That rug is from the den.

PHONICS

Part 6. Say Letters

Listen to the sound. Say the letter or letters that make that sound.

33.	39.	45.
34.	40.	46.
35.	41.	47.
36.	42.	48.
37.	43.	49.
38.	44.	50.

☼ Unit Checkpoint
Getting Stronger: Sounds /ă/, /ĕ/, /ĭ/, /ŏ/, and /ŭ/

Part 1. Say Sounds

Read across the row from left to right. Say a sound that letter makes.

1. e	2. y	3. u	4. i	5. x	6. a
7. w	8. o	9. x	10. a	11. u	12. y
13. i	14. u	15. y	16. w	17. e	18. x

Part 2. Word Dissection

Read the word. Circle the letter or group of letters that spell the sound you are asked to find.

19. r u g

20. w a x

21. y e t

22. f o x

23. w e t

PHONICS

Part 3. Finger Stretching

Listen to the word. Finger stretch the word.

24.

25.

26.

27.

28.

Part 4. Dictation

Listen to the word. Repeat the word, and then write it.

29. _____

30. _____

31. _____

32. _____

Part 5. Read Aloud

Read the sentences aloud.

33.

> Yes, Jim can run.
>
> The yak is at the vet.
>
> Put that pen in the cup.
>
> Tom says it is fun.
>
> There is a lot of gum.

PHONICS

Part 6. Say Letters

Listen to the sound. Say the letter or letters that make that sound.

PHONICS

34.	40.	46.
35.	41.	47.
36.	42.	48.
37.	43.	49.
38.	44.	50.
39.	45.	51.

☼ Unit Checkpoint
Review Short Vowels

Part 1. Say Sounds

Read across the row from left to right. Say a sound that the letter makes.

PHONICS

1. a	**2.** e	**3.** i	**4.** x	**5.** y	**6.** u

7. x	**8.** o	**9.** w	**10.** y	**11.** a	**12.** i

13. w	**14.** u	**15.** y	**16.** o	**17.** e	**18.** x

Part 2. Word Dissection

Read the word. Circle the letter or group of letters that spell the sound you are asked to find.

19. w i t

20. c u p

21. y e s

22. b o x

23. t a b

Part 3. Finger Stretching

Listen to the word. Finger stretch the word.

24.

25.

26.

27.

28.

PHONICS

Part 4. Dictation

Listen to the word. Repeat the word, and then write it.

29. _____

30. _____

31. _____

32. _____

PHONICS

Part 5. Read Aloud

Read the sentences aloud.

33.

> That dog can run!
>
> He has two pets.
>
> They both fix it.
>
> Put the tin can in the box.
>
> I have a lot of gum.

PHONICS

Part 6. Say Letters

Listen to the sound. Say the letter or letters that make that sound.

34.	40.	46.
35.	41.	47.
36.	42.	48.
37.	43.	49.
38.	44.	50.
39.	45.	51.

Unit Checkpoint
Getting Stronger: Short Vowels

PHONICS

Part 1. Say Sounds

Read across the row from left to right. Say a sound that the letter makes.

1. a	**2.** e	**3.** i	**4.** o	**5.** u	**6.** y
7. w	**8.** x	**9.** z	**10.** e	**11.** y	**12.** o
13. i	**14.** u	**15.** y	**16.** w	**17.** u	**18.** x

Part 2. Word Dissection

Read the word. Circle the letter or group of letters that spell the sound you are asked to find.

19. b u n

20. s i x

21. y e s

22. b o x

23. w e b

Part 3. Finger Stretching

Listen to the word. Finger stretch the word.

24.

25.

26.

27.

28.

Part 4. Dictation

Listen to the word. Repeat the word, and then write it.

29. _____

30. _____

31. _____

32. _____

PHONICS

Part 5. Read Aloud

Read the sentences aloud.

33.

Ten men can run.

The bed is in the den.

Tim fed his pup.

Did Dan let Ted in yet?

Kim can get in.

PHONICS

☼ Unit Checkpoint
Digraphs *sh* and *th*

Part 1. Say Sounds

Read across the row from left to right. Say a sound or sounds that the letter, letters, or word part makes.

1. –ish	**2.** –osh	**3.** –ush
4. –ash	**5.** –esh	**6.** –ith
7. –eth	**8.** –ath	**9.** –oth
10. –uth	**11.** x	**12.** r
13. l	**14.** w	**15.** qu
16. y	**17.** b	**18.** k

Part 2. Word Dissection

Read the word. Circle the letter or group of letters that spell the sound you are asked to find.

19. f i s h

20. s h i p

21. b a t h

22. t h i n

23. s h e d

PHONICS

Part 3. Finger Stretching

Listen to the word. Finger stretch the word.

24.

25.

26.

27.

28.

29.

Part 4. Dictation

Listen to the word. Repeat the word, and then write it.

30. _____

31. _____

32. _____

33. _____

PHONICS

Part 5. Read Aloud

Read the sentences aloud.

34.

> There is a big fish on that dish.
>
> Dad says we have to rush.
>
> Seth went with you.
>
> Where is the path?

PHONICS

PHONICS

Part 6. Say Letters

Listen to the sound. Say the letter or letters that make that sound.

35.

36.

37.

38.

39.

40.

41.

42.

43.

44.

45.

46.

47.

48.

49.

50.

51.

52.

☼ Unit Checkpoint
Getting Stronger: Short Vowels and Digraphs

Part 1. Say Sounds

Read across the row from left to right. Say a sound or sounds that the letter, letters, or word part makes.

1. –ash	**2.** –esh	**3.** –ush
4. –osh	**5.** –ish	**6.** –ath
7. –uth	**8.** –ith	**9.** –oth
10. –eth	**11.** k	**12.** w
13. r	**14.** l	**15.** qu
16. y	**17.** b	**18.** x

Part 2. Word Dissection

Read the word. Circle the letter or group of letters that spell the sound you are asked to find.

19. d i s h

20. s h i n

21. w i t h

22. t h e n

23. s h a g

Part 3. Finger Stretching

Listen to the word. Finger stretch the word.

24.

25.

26.

27.

28.

29.

PHONICS

Part 4. Dictation

Listen to the word. Repeat the word, and then write it.

PHONICS

30. _____

31. _____

32. _____

33. _____

Part 5. Read Aloud

Read the sentences aloud.

34.

> The rash is red.
>
> Then rush to the shed.
>
> I had cash in the dish.
>
> Josh has a wish.
>
> Beth went to the shop.

PHONICS

Part 6. Say Letters

Listen to the sound. Say the letter or letters that make that sound.

35.	41.	47.
36.	42.	48.
37.	43.	49.
38.	44.	50.
39.	45.	51.
40.	46.	52.

☼ Unit Checkpoint
Digraphs *wh* and *ch*

Part 1. Read Word Parts, Nonsense Words, and Words

Read across the row from left to right. Say the sounds of the word part, nonsense word, or word.

1. –ich	2. –wis	3. –ach
4. –chiz	5. –chob	6. –ich
7. chum	8. shop	9. –uth
10. –osh	11. wed	12. chum
13. fush	14. –ath	15. –ish
16. –ith	17. –oth	18. fish

Part 2. Word Dissection

Read the word. Circle the letter or group of letters that spell the sound you are asked to find.

19. w h i p

20. c h o p

21. s u c h

22. w h i z

23. w h i c h

PHONICS

Name   Date

Part 3. Finger Stretching

Listen to the word. Finger stretch the word.

24.

25.

26.

27.

28.

29.

PHONICS

Part 4. Dictation

Listen to the word. Repeat the word, and then write it.

PHONICS

30. _____

31. _____

32. _____

33. _____

34. _____

35. _____

Part 5. Read Aloud

Read the sentences aloud.

36.

> Chad has their dish.
>
> When did he chop that log?
>
> Which did you want?
>
> What is the rush, Chip?
>
> Kim is a whiz at math.

PHONICS

Part 6. Say Letters

Listen to the sound. Say the letter or letters that make that sound.

37.	43.	49.
38.	44.	50.
39.	45.	51.
40.	46.	52.
41.	47.	53.
42.	48.	54.

☼ Unit Checkpoint
Getting Stronger: Letter Sounds

Part 1. Read Word Parts and Nonsense Words

Read across the row from left to right. Say the sounds of the word part or nonsense word.

1. chun	**2.** wib	**3.** wan
4. wob	**5.** weg	**6.** shog
7. uch	**8.** thag	**9.** –ich
10. chid	**11.** shoth	**12.** chep
13. –ush	**14.** –ath	**15.** –ish
16. –ith	**17.** –oth	**18.** thib

Part 2. Word Dissection

Read the word. Circle the letter or group of letters that spell the sound you are asked to find.

19. c h u m

20. w h i z

21. r i c h

22. c h o p

23. w h i c h

PHONICS

Part 3. Finger Stretching

Listen to the word. Finger stretch the word.

24.

25.

26.

27.

28.

29.

PHONICS

Part 4. Dictation

Listen to the word. Repeat the word, and then write it.

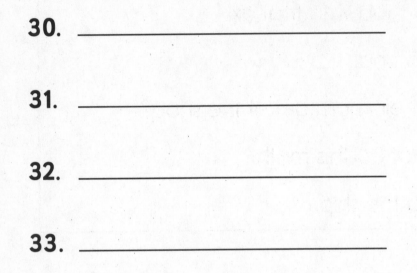

30. _____

31. _____

32. _____

33. _____

Part 5. Read Aloud

Read the sentences aloud.

34.

Chad can chop with that ax.

We want to chat.

What did their mom get at the shop?

Josh can not do this math.

We went to the ship.

PHONICS

Part 6. Say Letters

Listen to the sound. Say the letter or letters that make that sound.

35.

36.

37.

38.

39.

40.

41.

42.

43.

44.

45.

46.

47.

48.

49.

50.

51.

52.

☼ Unit Checkpoint
Trigraph –*tch* and Ending –*ck*

Part 1. Read Word Parts and Nonsense Words

Read across the row from left to right. Say the sounds of the word part or nonsense word.

1. –ick	**2.** –ack	**3.** –uck
4. –ock	**5.** –eck	**6.** –itch
7. –ach	**8.** –och	**9.** –ech
10. –ach	**11.** wheg	**12.** –ish
13. –ich	**14.** –ith	**15.** shog
16. chag	**17.** thig	**18.** –ath

Part 2. Word Dissection

Read the word. Circle the letter or group of letters that spell the sound you are asked to find.

19. i t c h

20. c a t c h

21. f e t c h

22. q u i c k

23. b a c k

PHONICS

Part 3. Finger Stretching

Listen to the word. Finger stretch the word.

24.

25.

26.

27.

28.

29.

PHONICS

PHONICS

Part 4. Dictation

Listen to the word. Repeat the word, and then write it.

30. _____

31. _____

32. _____

33. _____

Part 5. Read Aloud

Read the sentences aloud.

34.

Jack can pitch to Mitch.

Dad is quick to catch the duck.

Mom said your sock is in the back.

He will check on Nick.

Their ditch is so big.

Part 6. Say Letters

Listen to the sound. Say the letter or letters that make that sound.

35.

36.

37.

38.

39.

40.

41.

42.

43.

44.

45.

46.

47.

48.

49.

50.

51.

52.

☼ Unit Checkpoint
Getting Stronger: Digraphs, Trigraph *–tch*, and Ending *–ck*

Part 1. Read Word Parts, Nonsense Words, and Words

Read across the row from left to right. Say the sounds of the word part, nonsense word, or word.

1. –ick	**2.** chat	**3.** –uck
4. chit	**5.** shot	**6.** thit
7. shut	**8.** whit	**9.** –ush
10. –uch	**11.** wet	**12.** –ish
13. –uck	**14.** –ich	**15.** –ach
16. –ech	**17.** –ock	**18.** –ath

Part 2. Word Dissection

Read the word. Circle the letter or group of letters that spell the sound you are asked to find.

19. w i t h

20. c h a p

21. c a t c h

22. w h i z

23. c a s h

Part 3. Finger Stretching

Listen to the word. Finger stretch the word.

24.

25.

26.

27.

28.

29.

PHONICS

Part 4. Dictation

Listen to the word. Repeat the word, and then write it.

30. _____

31. _____

32. _____

33. _____

Part 5. Read Aloud

Read the sentences aloud.

34.

> Where is your batch of jam?
>
> Can Jack catch it?
>
> Mitch has a check for you.
>
> Did the duck quack?
>
> That chap has a rash on his neck.

Part 6. Say Letters

Listen to the sound. Say the letter or letters that make that sound.

35.

36.

37.

38.

39.

40.

41.

42.

43.

44.

45.

46.

47.

48.

☼ Unit Checkpoint
Review Digraphs and the Trigraph –tch

Part 1. Read Word Parts and Nonsense Words

Read across the row from left to right. Say the sounds of the word part or nonsense word.

1. –ack	2. chig	3. –ick
4. chob	5. shob	6. thim
7. sheg	8. whib	9. –ush
10. –uch	11. wez	12. –ish
13. –ock	14. –otch	15. –etch
16. atch	17. –uck	18. –ith

Part 2. Word Dissection

Read the word. Circle the letter or group of letters that spell the sound you are asked to find.

PHONICS

19. w h e n

20. c h o p

21. b a t c h

22. w h i p

23. s o c k

Part 3. Finger Stretching

Listen to the word. Finger stretch the word.

24.

25.

26.

27.

28.

29.

PHONICS

Part 4. Dictation

Listen to the word. Repeat the word, and then write it.

30. _____

31. _____

32. _____

33. _____

Part 5. Read Aloud
Read the sentences aloud.

34.

> Jack had an itch on his leg.
>
> Who went with Chuck to the shop?
>
> Where is the patch?
>
> Fetch the dish from the deck.
>
> Did you see a latch or lock?

Part 6. Say Letters

Listen to the sound. Say the letter or letters that make that sound.

35.	41.	47.
36.	42.	48.
37.	43.	49.
38.	44.	50.
39.	45.	51.
40.	46.	52.

Name   Date

Unit Checkpoint
Getting Stronger: Digraphs and the Trigraph –tch

Part 1. Read Word Parts, Nonsense Words, and Words

Read across the row from left to right. Say the sounds of the word part, nonsense word, or word.

1. eck	2. chat	3. –ock
4. chig	5. shun	6. thap
7. shut	8. whis	9. –esh
10. –och	11. weg	12. –ish
13. –ack	14. –otch	15. itch
16. etch	17. –uck	18. –ath

Part 2. Word Dissection

Read the word. Circle the letter or group of letters that spell the sound you are asked to find.

19. w h i z

20. c h i p

21. l a t c h

22. s h o p

23. t u c k

Part 3. Finger Stretching

Listen to the word. Finger stretch the word.

24.

25.

26.

27.

28.

29.

PHONICS

Part 4. Dictation

Listen to the word. Repeat the word, and then write it.

30. _____

31. _____

32. _____

33. _____

Part 5. Read Aloud

Read the sentences aloud.

34.

> Rick had luck to catch a fish.
>
> The hen can hatch a chick.
>
> His wish was a shock.
>
> The jam is thick.
>
> Beth said your mat is in the sack.

PHONICS

Part 6. Say Letters

Listen to the sound. Say the letter or letters that make that sound.

35.	41.	47.
36.	42.	48.
37.	43.	49.
38.	44.	50.
39.	45.	51.
40.	46.	52.

☼ Unit Checkpoint
Telling and Asking Sentences

Part 1. Say Sounds

Read across the row from left to right. Say a sound that the letter, letters, or digraph makes.

1. sh	**2.** th	**3.** ch	**4.** w *or* wh
5. c, k, *or* ck	**6.** b	**7.** a	**8.** i
9. o	**10.** u	**11.** e	**12.** f
13. r	**14.** w *or* wh	**15.** y	**16.** qu
17. x	**18.** p	**19.** m	**20.** n

Part 2. Word Dissection

Read the word. Circle the letter or group of letters that spell the sound you are asked to find.

21. s h e d

22. w i s h

23. p a t h

24. c h i p

25. c h e c k

Part 3. Finger Stretching

Listen to the word. Finger stretch the word.

26.

27.

28.

29.

30.

31.

PHONICS

Part 4. Writing: Periods and Question Marks

Complete each telling sentence with a period and each asking sentence with a question mark.

32. Pam has a hot dog ____

33. Can Mac catch Gus ____

34. Did Dad chop the log ____

35. The duck can quack ____

36. The fish is wet ____

37. Is Kim sick ____

PHONICS

Part 5. Read Aloud

Read the sentences aloud.

38.

She can run to Josh.

Can Meg pack her bag?

That was not a bug.

Sam has a gash on his leg.

Did you wish for a pet?

Part 6. Say Letters

Listen to the sound. Say the letter or letters that make that sound.

39.	45.	51.
40.	46.	52.
41.	47.	53.
42.	48.	54.
43.	49.	55.
44.	50.	56.

Unit Checkpoint
Getting Stronger: Short Vowels, Digraphs, and Sentences

Part 1. Say Sounds

Read across the row from left to right. Say a sound that the letter, letters, or digraph makes.

1. sh	**2.** th	**3.** ch	**4.** w *or* wh
5. c, k, *or* ck	**6.** a	**7.** i	**8.** ch
9. d	**10.** y	**11.** g	**12.** qu
13. f	**14.** p	**15.** m	**16.** qu
17. x	**18.** b	**19.** z	**20.** u

Part 2. Word Dissection

Read the word. Circle the letter or group of letters that spell the sound you are asked to find.

21. s h u t

22. d i s h

23. m a t c h

24. c h i n

25. w h e n

Part 3. Finger Stretching

Listen to the word. Finger stretch the word.

26.

27.

28.

29.

30.

31.

PHONICS

Part 4. Writing: Periods and Question Marks

Complete each telling sentence with a period and each asking sentence with a question mark.

32. Tim has a big log ____

33. Can Pam catch Bob ____

34. Did Mom tip the cup ____

35. Can the duck quack ____

36. The dish is wet ____

37. Is Jack sick ____

Part 5. Read Aloud

Read the sentences aloud.

38.

> Chad can hop to the mat.
>
> Can she run with her dog?
>
> Was that a shock?
>
> Beth has a hutch for her duck.
>
> Did the tot have her bath yet?

PHONICS

Part 6. Say Letters

Listen to the sound. Say the letter or letters that make that sound.

39.	45.	51.
40.	46.	52.
41.	47.	53.
42.	48.	54.
43.	49.	55.
44.	50.	56.

☼ Unit Checkpoint
Endings –s and –es

Part 1. Say Sounds

Read across the row from left to right. Say a sound that the letter, letters, or digraph makes.

1. sh	**2.** th	**3.** ch	**4.** w *or* wh
5. c, k, *or* ck	**6.** a	**7.** e	**8.** i
9. o	**10.** u	**11.** w	**12.** x
13. y	**14.** z	**15.** v	**16.** qu
17. b	**18.** d	**19.** p	**20.** g

Part 2. Find the Base Word

Underline the base word in the word.

21. checks

22. paths

23. cups

24. wishes

25. dishes

26. hatches

Part 3. Finger Stretching

Listen to the word. Finger stretch the word.

27.

28.

29.

30.

31.

32.

PHONICS

Part 4. Correct the Sentence

Write the first word of the sentence with a capital letter.
Complete each telling sentence with a period and
each asking sentence with a question mark.

33. the _____ ships went to the dock ____

34. she _____ catches a fish ____

35. he _____ rushes to the shed ____

36. is _____ her sock big ____

37. your _____ chicks did not hatch yet ____

Part 5. Read Aloud

Read the sentences aloud.

38.

> Why does she have two rocks?
>
> Dad dashes to his van.
>
> The chick hatches.
>
> Mom rushes to the shops.
>
> She fetches one tin can.

PHONICS

Part 6. Say Letters

Listen to the sound. Say the letter or letters that make that sound.

39.	45.	51.
40.	46.	52.
41.	47.	53.
42.	48.	54.
43.	49.	55.
44.	50.	56.

☼ Unit Checkpoint
Getting Stronger: Vowels

Part 1. Say Sounds
Read across the row from left to right. Say a sound that the letter, letters, or digraph makes.

1. th	**2.** sh	**3.** ch	**4.** w *or* wh
5. c, k, *or* ck	**6.** a	**7.** e	**8.** i
9. o	**10.** u	**11.** qu	**12.** w
13. v	**14.** x	**15.** p	**16.** b
17. z	**18.** y	**19.** g	**20.** d

Part 2. Find the Vowel

Underline the vowel in the word.

21. chick

22. bath

23. cap

24. dish

25. wish

26. latch

Part 3. Finger Stretching

Listen to the word. Finger stretch the word. Spell the ending.

27.

28.

29.

30.

31.

32.

PHONICS

Part 4. Correct the Sentence

Write the first word of the sentence with a capital letter.
Complete each telling sentence with a period and
each asking sentence with a question mark.

33. the _____ duck can quack _____

34. she _____ wishes for a dog _____

35. he _____ rushes to the van _____

36. is _____ your hat on top _____

37. which _____ one is my sack _____

Part 5. Read Aloud

Read the sentences aloud.

38.

Pam has six cats.

Mom dashes to catch her bus.

Does this sock match that one?

Dad fishes from the rock.

The dog fetches one log.

PHONICS

PHONICS

Part 6. Say Letters

Listen to the sound. Say the letter or letters that make that sound.

39.	**45.**	**51.**
40.	**46.**	**52.**
41.	**47.**	**53.**
42.	**48.**	**54.**
43.	**49.**	**55.**
44.	**50.**	**56.**

☼ Unit Checkpoint
Endings *–ff*, *–ll*, *–ss*, *–zz*, and *–all*

Part 1. Read Words and Word Parts

Read across the row from left to right. Say the sound or sounds of the word or word part.

1. –ish	**2.** all	**3.** –ull
4. –aff	**5.** –uff	**6.** –uss
7. –eff	**8.** if	**9.** –oss
10. us	**11.** –es	**12.** –iss
13. –azz	**14.** –izz	**15.** –off
16. –uzz	**17.** –atch	**18.** –ock

Part 2. Finger Stretching

Listen to the word. Finger stretch the word.

19.

20.

21.

22.

23.

24.

PHONICS

Part 3. Dictation

Listen to the word. Repeat the word, and then write it.

25. _____

26. _____

27. _____

28. _____

29. _____

30. _____

PHONICS

Part 4. Read Aloud

Read the sentences aloud.

31.

> Do not fall off the wall.
>
> The dolls were in your bag.
>
> Are Russ and Bill chums?
>
> Jeff will huff and puff up the hill.
>
> My pets can buzz and hiss.

LANGUAGE ARTS BLUE | ENDINGS –ff, –ll, –ss, –zz, AND –all

Part 5. Say Letters

Listen to the sound. Say the letter or letters that make that sound.

32.

33.

34.

35.

36.

37.

38.

39.

40.

✧ Unit Checkpoint
Compound Words

Part 1. Read Word Parts

Read across the row from left to right. Say the sounds of
the word part.

1. –osh	**2.** –aff	**3.** –ull
4. –ell	**5.** –atch	**6.** –ish
7. –es	**8.** –oss	**9.** –uss
10. –iss	**11.** –eff	**12.** –iff
13. –ith	**14.** –uzz	**15.** –ull
16. –azz	**17.** –izz	**18.** –ozz

Part 2. Finger Stretching

Listen to the word. Finger stretch the word.

PHONICS

19.

20.

21.

22.

23.

24.

25.

26.

Part 3. Dictation

Listen to the word. Repeat the word, and then write it.

27. _____

28. _____

29. _____

30. _____

31. _____

32. _____

Part 4. Writing

Listen to the sentence. Repeat the sentence, and then write it.

33. _____

34. _____

Part 5. Read Aloud

Read the sentences aloud.

35.

Dr. Nack will get that laptop.

There is mud in the pigpen.

Mrs. Ratch has a hat in the hatbox.

Will Mr. Bazz fill this backpack?

PHONICS

Part 6. Say Letters

Listen to the sound. Say the letter or letters that make that sound.

36.	39.	42.
37.	40.	43.
38.	41.	44.

Unit Checkpoint
Getting Stronger: Sentences, Endings, and Compound Words

Part 1. Read Word Parts

Read across the row from left to right. Say the sounds of the word part.

1. –aches

2. –itch

3. –ech

4. –ull

5. –ells

6. –ill

7. –oll

8. –aff

9. –iff

10. –uff

11. –ess

12. –iss

13. –ess

14. –azz

15. –uzzes

16. –ish

17. –ith

18. –oth

Part 2. Finger Stretching

Listen to the word. Finger stretch the word.

19.

20.

21.

22.

23.

24.

25.

26.

Part 3. Dictation

Listen to the word. Repeat the word, and then write it.

27. _____

28. _____

29. _____

30. _____

31. _____

32. _____

PHONICS

Part 4. Writing

Listen to the sentence. Repeat the sentence, and then write it.

33. _____

34. _____

PHONICS

Part 5. Read Aloud

Read the sentences aloud.

35.

Jen wishes for a laptop.

Why is her doll in there?

The pigs cannot get in the pigpen.

Are you on the hilltop?

Part 6. Say Letters

Listen to the sound. Say the letter or letters that make that sound.

36.

37.

38.

39.

40.

41.

42.

43.

44.

☼ Unit Checkpoint
Words, Letters & Sounds, and Sentences

Part 1. Read Word Parts

Read across the row from left to right. Say the sounds of the word part.

1. –azz	**2.** –izz	**3.** –uzz
4. –ell	**5.** –ill	**6.** –oll
7. –ull	**8.** –ash	**9.** –ath
10. –ish	**11.** –ith	**12.** –oth
13. –ess	**14.** –iss	**15.** –uss
16. –ick	**17.** –ich	**18.** –otch

Part 2. Finger Stretching

Listen to the word. Finger stretch the word.

19.

20.

21.

22.

23.

24.

25.

26.

PHONICS

Part 3. Dictation

Listen to the word. Repeat the word, and then write it.

27. _____

28. _____

29. _____

30. _____

31. _____

32. _____

PHONICS

Part 4. Writing

Listen to the sentence. Repeat the sentence, and then write it.

33. _____

34. _____

Part 5. Read Aloud

Read the sentences aloud.

35.

> Mr. Wills went to shop.
>
> Are Jack and Bess on the deck?
>
> Where is that buzz from?
>
> She said her pet was ill.
>
> Where did you put your backpack?

PHONICS

Part 6. Say Letters

Listen to the sound. Say the letter or letters that make that sound.

36.

37.

38.

39.

40.

41.

42.

43.

44.